THE DRUM

An Indian Folktale

retold by Betsy Franco

illustrated by Steven Royal

HARCOURT BRACE & COMPANY

Orlando   Atlanta   Austin   Boston   San Francisco   Chicago   Dallas   New York
Toronto   London

Ram wanted a drum
so he could play ra-tat-tat-tum.

One day Ram found a stick.
Ti-ti-ti.

3

Ram gave the stick to a woman,
who gave him some bread.
Yum, yum, yum.

4

Ram gave the bread to a girl,
who gave him a jar.
Plink, plink, plink.

Ram gave the jar to a man,
who gave him a coat.
Swish, swish, swish.

6

Ram gave the coat to a groom,
who gave him a beautiful drum!
Ra-tat-tat-tum.

Ram walked with his drum.
Ra-tat-tat-tum. Ra-tat-tat-tum,
Ra-tat-tat-Ra-tat-tat-tum.

Ram saw the man with the jar.
Ra-tat-tat-tum.

Ram saw the girl with the bread.
Ra-tat-tat-tum.

Ram saw the woman with the stick.
Ra-tat-tat-tum.

Ram played his beautiful drum.
Ra-tat-tat-tum. Ra-tat-tat-tum,
Ra-tat-tat-Ra-tat-tat-tum.